To Daniel —
with all my lo
coring, in the fl
your own fascinating,
Mom
1/11/77

D0442150

Herman Melville:
VOYAGES

Selected and With a Commentary by

Stanley Hendricks

HALLMARK EDITIONS

"I Love Sleepy Fellows" reprinted by permission of the publishers from Eleanor Melville Metcalf, *Herman Melville: Cycle and Epicycle*, Cambridge, Mass.: Harvard University Press, Copyright, 1953, by the President and Fellows of Harvard College. "A Siamese Link of Affectionate Sympathy" by Herman Melville from *The Portable Melville*, edited by Jay Leyda. Reprinted by permission of the Massachusetts Historical Society. Printed in the United States of America. Library of Congress Catalog Card Number: 72-122359. Standard Book Number: 87529-109-0.

HERMAN MELVILLE: VOYAGES

TYPEE, A PEEP AT POLYNESIAN LIFE

In 1841, New Yorker Herman Melville sailed out of Liverpool on the whaler *Acushnet* for what was to be a three-year voyage as an ordinary seaman. He was twenty-three years old. The long whaling voyage would give him the foundation of knowledge he would later use to write his greatest novel, *Moby Dick*, but other works preceded that masterpiece. The first was *Typee*. In July, 1842, in the Marquesa Islands of the Pacific, Melville and a friend jumped ship and lived for a month with a tribe of cannibals. That experience formed the basis for his first novel, written, so he said, at the urging of friends who listened to his yarns after his return to the United States in 1844. The story is narrated by a sailor named Tom, who stands for Melville himself. Early in the book, Tom's ship is lying at harbor near several French ships. Seeking control of the Islands, the French are paying court to a native king, Mowanna, and his queen. The following incident, involving the queen's tattoos, shocked and secretly fascinated the readers of Melville's day.

One bright afternoon, a gig, gaily bedizened with streamers, was observed to shove off from the side of one of the French frigates, and pull directly for our gangway. In the stern sheets reclined Mowanna and his consort. As they approached, we paid them all the honors due to royalty;— manning our yards, firing a salute, and making prodigious hubbub.

They ascended the accommodation ladder, were greeted by the Commodore, hat in hand, and passing along the quarterdeck, the marine guard presented arms, while the band struck up "The King of the Cannibal Islands." So far all went well. The French officers grimaced and smiled in exceedingly high spirits, wonderfully pleased with the discreet manner in which these distinguished personages behaved themselves.

Their appearance was certainly calculated to produce

an effect. His majesty was arrayed in a magnificent military uniform, stiff with gold lace and embroidery, while his shaven crown was concealed by a huge chapeau bras, waving with ostrich plumes. There was one slight blemish, however, in his appearance. A broad patch of tatooing stretched completely across his face, in a line with his eyes, making him look as if he wore a huge pair of goggles; and royalty in goggles suggested some ludicrous ideas. But it was in the adornment of the fair person of his dark-complexioned spouse that the tailors of the fleet had evinced the gaiety of their national taste. She was habited in a gaudy tissue of scarlet cloth, trimmed with yellow silk, which descending a little below the knees, exposed to view her bare legs, embellished with spiral tattooing, and somewhat resembling two miniature Trajan's columns. Upon her head was a fanciful turban of purple velvet, figured with silver springs, and surmounted by a tuft of variegated feathers.

The ship's company crowding into the gangway to view the sight, soon arrested her majesty's attention. She singled out from their number an old *salt*, whose bare arms and feet, and exposed breast, were covered with as many inscriptions in India ink, as the lid of an Egyptian sarcophagus. Notwithstanding all the sly hints and remonstrances of the French officers, she immediately approached the man, and pulling further open the bosom of his duck frock, and rolling up the leg of his wide trowsers, she gazed with admiration at the bright blue and vermillion pricking thus disclosed to view. She hung over the fellow, caressing him, and expressing her delight in a variety of wild exclamations and gestures. The embarrassment of the polite Gauls at such an unlooked-for occurrence may be easily imagined; but picture their consternation, when all at once the royal lady bent eagerly forward to display the hieroglyphics on her own sweet form, and the aghast Frenchmen retreated precipitately, and tumbling into their boat, fled the scene of so shocking a catastrophe.

'GETTING THE FIRE READY'

Tom, *Typee*'s narrator, and his friend Toby jump ship and are welcomed by a tribe they at first believe to be the friendly Happars but who turn out to be the cannibalistic Typees. One of the tribe's chiefs, Mehevi, accords Tom and Toby warm treatment, assigning a tribesman, Kory-Kory, to Tom as a personal attendant. The sailors are nevertheless apprehensive of the reasons for the natives' friendly care.

When Mehevi had departed from the house, as related in the preceding chapter, Kory-Kory commenced the functions of the post assigned him. He brought us various kinds of food; and, as if I were an infant, insisted upon feeding me with his own hands. To this procedure I, of course, most earnestly objected, but in vain; and having laid a calabash of Kokoo before me, he washed his fingers in a vessel of water, and then putting his hand into the dish and rolling the food into little balls, put them one after another into my mouth. All my remonstrances against this measure only provoked so great a clamor on his part, that I was obliged to acquiesce; and the operation of feeding being thus facilitated, the meal was quickly despatched. As for Toby, he was allowed to help himself after his own fashion.

The repast over, my attendant arranged the mats for

repose, and, bidding me lie down, covered me with a large robe of tappa, at the same time looking approvingly upon me, and exclaiming "Ki-Ki, muee muee, ah! moee moee mortarkee" (eat plenty, ah! sleep very good). The philosophy of this sentiment I did not pretend to question; for, deprived of sleep for several preceding nights, and the pain of my limb* having much abated, I now felt inclined to avail myself of the opportunity afforded me.

The next morning, on waking, I found Kory-Kory stretched out on one side of me, while my companion lay upon the other. I felt sensibly refreshed after a night of sound repose, and immediately agreed to the proposition of my valet that I should repair to the water and wash, although dreading the suffering that the exertion might produce. From this apprehension, however, I was quickly relieved; for Kory-Kory, leaping from the pi-pi,* and then backing himself up against it, like a porter in readiness to shoulder a trunk, with loud vociferations and a superabundance of gestures, gave me to understand that I was to mount upon his back and be thus transported to the stream, which flowed perhaps two hundred yards from the house.

Our appearance upon the veranda in front of the habitation drew together quite a crowd, who stood looking on and conversing with one another in the most animated manner. They reminded one of a group of idlers gathered about the door of a village tavern when the equipage of some distinguished traveller is brought round previous to his departure. As soon as I clasped my arms about the neck of the devoted fellow, and he jogged off with me, the

*Tom had earlier injured his leg.   *A native house.

crowd—composed chiefly of young girls and boys—followed after, shouting and capering with infinite glee, and accompanied us to the banks of the stream.

On gaining it, Kory-Kory, wading up to his hips in the water, carried me half way across, and deposited me on a smooth black stone which rose a few inches above the surface. The amphibious rabble at our heels plunged in after us, and climbing to the summit of the grass-grown rocks with which the bed of the brook was here and there broken, waited curiously to witness our morning ablutions.

Somewhat embarrassed by the presence of the female portion of the company, and feeling my cheeks burning with bashful timidity, I formed a primitive basin by joining my hands together, and cooled my blushes in the water it contained; then removing my frock, bent over and washed myself down to my waist in the stream. As soon as Kory-Kory comprehended from my motions that this was to be the extent of my performance, he appeared perfectly aghast with astonishment, and rushing towards me, poured out a torrent of words in eager deprecation of so limited an operation, enjoining me by unmistakable signs to immerse my whole body. To this I was forced to consent; and the honest fellow regarding me as a froward, inexperienced child, whom it was his duty to serve at the risk of offending, lifted me from the rock, and tenderly bathed my limbs. This over, and resuming my seat, I could not avoid bursting into admiration of the scene around me.

From the verdant surfaces of the large stones that lay scattered about, the natives were now sliding off into the water, diving and ducking beneath the surface in all directions; the young girls springing buoyantly into the air, and revealing their naked forms to the waist, with their long tresses dancing about their shoulders, their eyes sparkling like drops of dew in the sun, and their gay laughter pealing forth at every frolicsome incident.

On the afternoon of the day that I took my first bath in the valley, we received another visit from Mehevi. The noble savage seemed to be in the same pleasant mood, and was quite as cordial in his manner as before. After remaining about an hour, he rose from the mats, and motioning to leave the house, invited Toby and myself to accompany him. I pointed to my leg; but Mehevi in his turn pointed to Kory-Kory, and removed that objection; so, mounting upon the faithful fellow's shoulders again—like the old man of the sea astride of Sinbad—I followed after the chief. . . .

After proceeding a little distance—Kory-Kory panting and blowing with the weight of his burden—I dismounted from his back, and grasping the long spear of Mehevi in my hand, assisted my steps over the numerous obstacles of the road; preferring this mode of advance to one which, from the difficulties of the way, was equally painful to myself and my wearied servitor.

Our journey was soon at an end; for, scaling a sudden height, we came abruptly upon the place of our destination. I wish that it were possible to sketch in words this spot as vividly as I recollect it.

Here were situated the Taboo groves of the valley—the scene of many a prolonged feast, of many a horrid rite. Beneath the dark shadows of the consecrated bread-fruit trees there reigned a solemn twilight—a cathedral-like gloom. The frightful genius of pagan worship seemed to brood in silence over the place, breathing its spell upon every object around. Here and there, in the depths of these awful shades, half screened from sight by masses of overhanging foliage, rose the idolatrous altars of the savages, built of enormous blocks of black and polished stone, placed one upon another, without cement, to the height of twelve or fifteen feet, and surmounted by a rustic open temple, enclosed with a low picket of canes, within which might be seen, in various stages of decay, offerings of bread-fruit and cocoa-nuts, and the putrifying relics of some recent sacrifice.

In the midst of the wood was the hallowed "hoolah hoolah" ground—set apart for the celebration of the fantastical religious ritual of these people—comprising an extensive oblong pi-pi terminating at either end in a lofty terraced altar, guarded by ranks of hideous wooden idols, and with the two remaining sides flanked by ranges of bamboo sheds, opening towards the interior of the quadrangle thus formed. Vast trees, standing in the middle of this space, and throwing over it an umbrageous shade, had their massive trunks built round with slight stages, elevated a few feet above the ground, and railed in with canes, forming so many rustic pulpits, from which the priests harangued their devotees.

This holiest of spots was defended from profanation by the strictest edicts of the all-prevading "taboo," which condemned to instant death the sacrilegious female who should enter or touch its sacred precincts, or even so much as press with her feet the ground made holy by the shadows that it cast.

Access was had to the enclosure through an embowered
entrance on one side, facing a number of towering cocoa-
nut trees, planted at intervals along a level area of a hundred yards. At the further extremity of this space was to
be seen a building of considerable size, reserved for the
habitation of the priests and religious attendants of the
groves.

In its vicinity was another remarkable edifice, built as
usual upon the summit of a pi-pi, and at least two hundred
feet in length, though not more than twenty in breadth.
The whole front of this latter structure was completely
open, and from one end to the other ran a narrow veranda, fenced in on the edge of the pi-pi with a picket of
canes. Its interior presented the appearance of an immense
lounging place, the entire floor being strewn with succes-
sive layers of mats, lying between parallel trunks of cocoa-
nut trees, selected for the purpose from the straightest and
most symmetrical the vale afforded.

To this building, denominated in the language of the
natives the "Ti," Mehevi now conducted us. Thus far we
had been accompanied by a troop of the natives of both
sexes; but as soon as we approached its vicinity, the fe-
males gradually separated themselves from the crowd, and
standing aloof, permitted us to pass on. The merciless pro-
hibitions of the taboo extended likewise to this edifice, and
were enforced by the same dreadful penalty that secured
the hoolah hoolah ground from the imaginary pollution
of a woman's presence.

On entering the house, I was surprised to see six muskets
ranged against the bamboo on one side, from the barrels
of which depended as many small canvas pouches, partly

filled with powder. Disposed about these muskets, like the cutlasses that decorate the bulkhead of a man-of-war's cabin, were a great variety of rude spears and paddles, javelins, and war-clubs. This then, said I to Toby, must be the armory of the tribe.

As we advanced further along the building, we were struck with the aspect of four or five hideous old wretches, on whose decrepit forms time and tattooing seemed to have obliterated every trace of humanity. . . .

These repulsive-looking creatures appeared to have lost the use of their lower limbs altogether, sitting upon the floor crosslegged in a state of torpor. They never heeded us in the least, scarcely looking conscious of our presence, while Mehevi seated us upon the mats, and Kory-Kory gave utterance to some unintelligible gibberish.

In a few moments a boy entered with a wooden trencher of poee-poee; and in regaling myself with its contents I was obliged again to submit to the officious intervention of my indefatigable servitor. Various other dishes followed, the chief manifesting the most hospitable importunity in pressing us to partake, and to remove all bashfulness on our part, set us no despicable example in his own person.

The repast concluded, a pipe was lighted, which passed from mouth to mouth, and yielding to its soporific influence, the quiet of the place, and the deepening shadows of approaching night, my companion and I sank into a kind of drowsy repose, while the chief and Kory-Kory seemed to be slumbering beside us.

I awoke from an uneasy nap, about midnight, as I supposed; and, raising myself partly from the mat, became sensible that we were enveloped in utter darkness. Toby lay still asleep, but our late companions had disappeared. The only sound that interrupted the silence of the place was the asthmatic breathing of the old men I have mentioned, who reposed at a little distance from us. Besides them, as well as I could judge, there was no one else in the house.

Apprehensive of some evil, I roused my comrade, and we were engaged in a whispered conference concerning the unexpected withdrawal of the natives, when all at once, from the depths of the grove, in full view of us where we lay, shoots of flame were seen to rise, and in a few moments illuminated the surrounding trees, casting, by contrast, into still deeper gloom the darkness around us.

While we continued gazing at this sight, dark figures appeared moving to and fro before the flames; while others, dancing and capering about, looked like so many demons.

Regarding this new phenomenon with no small degree of trepidation, I said to my companion, "What can all this mean, Toby?"

"Oh, nothing," replied he; "getting the fire ready I suppose."

"Fire!" exclaimed I, while my heart took to beating like a triphammer, "what fire?"

"Why, the fire to cook us, to be sure; what else would the cannibals be kicking up such a row about if it were not for that?"

"Oh, Toby! have done with your jokes; this is no time for them; something is about to happen, I feel confident."

"Jokes, indeed!" exclaimed Toby indignantly. "Did you ever hear me joke? Why, for what do you suppose the devils have been feeding us up in this kind of style during the last three days, unless it were for something that you are too much frightened at to talk about? Look at that Kory-Kory there!—has he not been stuffing you with his confounded mushes, just in the way they treat swine before they kill them? Depend upon it, we will be eaten this blessed night, and there is the fire we shall be roasted by."

This view of the matter was not at all calculated to allay my apprehensions, and I shuddered when I reflected that we were indeed at the mercy of a tribe of cannibals, and that the dreadful contingency to which Toby had alluded was by no means removed beyond the bounds of possibility.

"There! I told you so! they are coming for us!" exclaimed my companion the next moment, as the forms of four of the islanders were seen in bold relief against the illuminated background, mounting the pi-pi and approaching towards us.

They came on noiselessly, nay stealthily, and glided along through the gloom that surrounded us as if about to spring upon some object they were fearful of disturbing before they should make sure of it.—Gracious heaven! the horrible reflections which crowded upon me that moment. —A cold sweat stood upon my brow, and spellbound with terror I awaited my fate!

Suddenly the silence was broken by the well-remembered tones of Mehevi, and at the kindly accents of his voice my fears were immediately dissipated. "Tommo, Toby, ki ki!" (eat). He had waited to address us, until he had assured himself that we were both awake, at which he seemed somewhat surprised.

"Ki, ki! is it?" said Toby in his gruff tones; "well, cook us first will you—but what's this?" he added, as another savage appeared, bearing before him a large trencher of wood, containing some kind of steaming meat, as appeared from the odors it diffused, and which he deposited at the feet of Mehevi. "A baked baby, I dare say! but I will have none of it, never mind what it is.—A pretty fool I should make of myself, indeed, waked up here in the middle of the night, stuffing and guzzling, and all to make a fat meal for a parcel of booby-minded cannibals one of these mornings!—No, I see what they are at very plainly, so I am resolved to starve myself into a bunch of bones and gristle, and then, if they serve me up, they are welcome! But I say, Tommo, you are not going to eat any of that mess there, in the dark, are you? Why, how can you tell what it is?"

"By tasting it, to be sure," said I, masticating a morsel that Kory-Kory had just put in my mouth; "and excellently good it is, too, very much like veal."

"A baked baby, by the soul of Captain Cook!" burst forth Toby, with amazing vehemence; "Veal, why, there never was a calf on the island till you landed. I tell you you are bolting down mouthfuls from a dead Happar's carcass, as sure as you live, and no mistake!"

Emetics and lukewarm water! What a sensation in the abdominal regions! Sure enough, where could the fiends incarnate have obtained meat? But I resolved to satisfy myself at all hazards; and turning to Mehevi, I soon made the ready chief understand that I wished a light to be brought. When the taper came, I gazed eagerly into the vessel, and recognized the mutilated remains of a juvenile

porker! "Puarkee!" exclaimed Kory-Kory, looking com-
placently at the dish; and from that day to this I have
never forgotten that such is the designation of a pig in the
Typee lingo.

'A SIAMESE LINK OF
AFFECTIONATE SYMPATHY'

Making good a hair-raising escape from the Typees, Melville and his
friend signed on to the whaler *Lucy Ann* and soon became involved in
a mutiny which failed. Later Melville was imprisoned on Tahiti, but
he managed to escape on another whaler and reached Honolulu. He
worked there briefly as a clerk, then, looking for more adventure,
joined the U.S. Navy and went aboard the frigate *United States*, due
to sail for Boston. He had not reckoned with the stern conditions
aboard a vessel of war, nor with the *United States'* lengthy course—
she visited the ports of Central and South America for more than a
year. By the time Melville reached Boston, having seen many
floggings and barely escaped flogging himself, he was ready to give
up the seafaring life. He published *Typee* to considerable acclaim in
1846. *Omoo* appeared the next year, *Redburn* and *Mardi* in 1849. That
year he also finished *White-Jacket*, which appeared in 1850. In three
years he had written five books. He began *Moby Dick*. He was then
30 years old. Here he writes, as an equal, to Richard Henry Dana, Jr.,
the distinguished author of *Two Years Before the Mast*, who had
sent Melville a letter warmly praising *Redburn* and *White-Jacket*.

New York, May 1, 1850

My Dear Dana: I thank you very heartily for your friendly letter; and am more pleased than I can well tell, to
think that anything I have written about the sea has at all
responded to your own impressions of it. Were I inclined
to undue vanity, this one fact would be far more to me
than acres and square miles of the superficial shallow

praise of the publishing critics. And I am especially delighted at the thought, that those strange, congenial feelings, with which after my first voyage, I for the first time read *Two Years Before the Mast*, and while so engaged was, as it were, tied and welded to you by a sort of Siamese link of affectionate sympathy—that these feelings should be reciprocated by you, in your turn, and be called out by any White Jackets or Redburns of mine—this is indeed delightful to me. In fact, my dear Dana, did I not write these books of mine almost entirely for "lucre"—by the job, as a wood sawyer saws wood—I almost think, I should hereafter—in the case of a sea book—get my M.S.S. neatly and legibly copied by a scrivener—send you that one copy —and deem such a procedure the best publication. . . .

About the "whaling voyage"—I am half way in the work, and am very glad that your suggestion so jumps with mine. It will be a strange sort of a book, tho', I fear; blubber is blubber you know; tho' you may get oil out of it, the poetry runs as hard as sap from a frozen maple tree; —and to cook the thing up, one must needs throw in a little fancy, which from the nature of the thing, must be ungainly as the gambols of the whales themselves. Yet I mean to give the truth of the thing, spite of this.

Give my compliments to Mrs. Dana, and remember me to your father.

Sincerely yours, *H. Melville*

'CALL ME ISHMAEL'

Moby Dick was Melville's greatest work, and many think it is also the greatest American fiction ever written. In Melville's own time it was greeted with total contempt as the misshapen, vulgar mistake of a once-competent author of South Sea tales. The mistake lay with *Moby Dick*'s critics, however: they failed to see that the book did not conform to the traditional restrictions of the novel because it was not a novel at all, but a massive, original chunk of language with the single purpose of seeing the entire universe through the point of view of a whaling voyage, or, more broadly, through the point of view of the mysteries of the sea. *Moby Dick* begins simply enough: a young man named Ishmael is hiking to New Bedford to sign on for a whaling voyage.

Call me Ishmael. Some years ago—never mind how long precisely—having little or no money in my purse, and nothing particular to interest me on shore, I thought I would sail about a little and see the watery part of the world. It is a way I have of driving off the spleen, and regulating the circulation. Whenever I find myself growing grim about the mouth; whenever it is damp, drizzly November in my soul; whenever I find myself involuntarily pausing before coffin warehouses, and bringing up the rear of every funeral I meet; and especially whenever my hypos get such an upper hand of me, that it requires a strong moral principle to prevent me from deliberately stepping into the street, and methodically knocking people's hats off—then, I account it high time to get to sea as soon as I can. This is my substitute for pistol and ball. With a philosophical flourish Cato throws himself upon his sword; I quietly take to the ship. There is nothing surprising in this. If they but knew it, almost all men in their degree, some time or other, cherish very nearly the same feelings towards the ocean with me. . . .

Though I cannot tell why it was exactly that those stage managers, the Fates, put me down for this shabby part of a whaling voyage, when others were set down for magnificent parts in high tragedies, and short and easy parts in genteel comedies, and jolly parts in farces—though I cannot tell why this was exactly; yet, now that I recall all the circumstances, I think I can see a little into the springs and motives which being cunningly presented to me under various disguises, induced me to set about performing the part I did, besides cajoling me into the delusion that it was a choice resulting from my own unbiassed freewill and discriminating judgment.

Chief among these motives was the overwhelming idea of the great whale himself. Such a portentous and mysterious monster roused all my curiosity. Then the wild and distant seas where he rolled his island bulk; the undeliverable, nameless perils of the whale; these, with all the attending marvels of a thousand Patagonian sights and sounds, helped to sway me to my wish. With other men, perhaps, such things would not have been inducements; but as for me, I am tormented with an everlasting itch for things remote. I love to sail forbidden seas, and land on barbarous coasts. Not ignoring what is good, I am quick to perceive a horror, and could still be sociable with it— would they let me—since it is but well to be on friendly terms with all the inmates of the place one lodges in.

By reason of these things, then, the whaling voyage was welcome; the great floodgates of the wonder-world swung open, and in the wild conceits that swayed me to my purpose, two and two there floated into my inmost soul, endless processions of the whale, and, midmost of them all, one grand hooded phantom, like a snow hill in the air.

'SHAPED IN AN UNALTERABLE MOULD'

Next to the great white whale itself, the most dominating figure in *Moby Dick* is Captain Ahab, the fierce commander of the *Pequod* who has set sail on a voyage of vengeance, to hunt down the whale who years before took away his leg. Ahab does not leave his cabin for several days after the voyage begins, but at last Ishmael catches sight of the Captain, and describes him in language filled with awe and more than a little terror.

It was one of those less lowering, but still grey and gloomy enough mornings of the transition, when with a fair wind the ship was rushing through the water with a vindictive sort of leaping and melancholy rapidity, that as I mounted to the deck at the call of the forenoon watch, so soon as I levelled my glance towards the taffrail, foreboding shivers ran over me. Reality outran apprehensions; Captain Ahab stood upon his quarter-deck.

There seemed no sign of common bodily illness about him, nor of the recovery from any. He looked like a man cut away from the stake, when the fire has overrunningly wasted all the limbs without consuming them, or taking away one particle from their compacted aged robustness. His whole high, broad form seemed made of solid bronze, and shaped in an unalterable mould, like Cellini's cast

Perseus. Threading its way out from among his grey hairs, and continuing right down one side of his tawny scorched face and neck, till it disappeared in his clothing, you saw a slender rod-like mark, lividly whitish. It resembled that perpendicular seam sometimes made in the straight, lofty trunk of a great tree, when the upper lightning tearingly darts down it, and without wrenching a single twig, peels and grooves out the bark from top to bottom, ere running off into the soil, leaving the tree still greenly alive, but branded. Whether that mark was born with him, or whether it was the scar left by some desperate wound, no one could certainly say. By some tacit consent, throughout the voyage little or no allusion was made to it, especially by the mates. But once Tashtego's senior, an old Gay-Head among the crew, superstitiously asserted that not till he was full forty years old did Ahab become that way branded, and then it came upon him, not in the fury of any mortal fray, but in an elemental strife at sea. Yet, this wild hint seemed inferentially negatived, by what a grey Manxman insinuated, an old sepulchral man, who, having never before sailed out of Nantucket, had never ere this laid eye upon wild Ahab. Nevertheless, the old sea-traditions, the immemorial credulities, popularly invested this old Manxman with preternatural powers of discernment. So that no white sailor seriously contradicted him when he said that if ever Captain Ahab should be tranquilly laid out—which might hardly come to pass, so he muttered—then, whoever should do that last office for the dead, would find a birthmark on him from crown to sole.

So powerfully did the whole grim aspect of Ahab affect me, and the livid brand which streaked it, that for the first

few moments I hardly noted that not a little of this overbearing grimness was owing to the barbaric white leg
upon which he partly stood. It had previously come to me
that this ivory leg had at sea been fashioned from the polished bone of the sperm whale's jaw. "Aye, he was dismasted off Japan," said the old Gay-Head Indian once;
"but like his dismasted craft, he shipped another mast
without coming home for it. He has a quiver of 'em."

I was struck with the singular posture he maintained.
Upon each side of the *Pequod*'s quarter-deck, and pretty
close to the mizzen shrouds, there was an auger hole, bored
about half an inch or so into the plank. His bone leg
steadied in that hole, one arm elevated, and holding by a
shroud, Captain Ahab stood erect, looking straight out beyond the ship's ever-pitching prow. There was an infinity
of firmest fortitude, a determinate, unsurrenderable wil-
fulness, in the fixed and fearless, forward dedication of
that glance. Not a word he spoke; nor did his officers say
aught to him; though by all their minutest gestures and
expression, they plainly showed the uneasy, if not painful,
consciousness of being under a troubled master-eye. And
not only that, but moody stricken Ahab stood before them
with a crucifixion in his face; in all the nameless regal
overbearing dignity of some mighty woe.

THE WHITENESS OF THE WHALE

Throughout *Moby Dick*, Melville from time to time turns away from direct narrative to consider the larger implications of whales and whaling. These digressions, which many critics have thought should be cut from the book, in fact expand its purpose with the subtlest philosophy, just as the *Old Testament*'s books of prophecy make it a work of larger meaning than simply the narrative of the history of Israel. In one digression, "The Whiteness of the Whale," Melville considers the sinister implications of whiteness in nature. "There yet lurks an elusive something in the innermost idea of this hue," he writes, "which strikes more of panic to the soul than that redness which affrights in blood." The chapter is a masterpiece of metaphoric association, drawing on Melville's profound imagination as well as his deep reading.

What the white whale was to Ahab, has been hinted; what at times, he was to me, as yet remains unsaid.

Aside from those more obvious considerations touching Moby Dick, which could not but occasionally awaken in any man's soul some alarm, there was another thought, or rather vague, nameless horror concerning him, which at times by its intensity completely overpowered all the rest; and yet so mystical and well-nigh ineffable was it, that I almost despair of putting it in a comprehensible form. It was the whiteness of the whale that above all things appalled me. But how can I hope to explain myself here; and yet, in some dim, random way, explain myself I must, else all these chapters might be naught.

Though in many natural objects, whiteness refiningly enhances beauty, as if imparting some special virtue of its own, as in marbles, japonicas, and pearls; and though various nations have in some way recognized a certain royal preeminence in this hue; even the barbaric, grand old kings of Pegu placing the title "Lord of White Elephants"

above all their other magniloquent ascriptions of domin-
ion; and the modern kings of Siam unfurling the same
snow-white quadruped in the royal standard; and the
Hanoverian flag bearing the one figure of a snow-white
charger; and the great Austrian Empire, Caesarian heir
to overlording Rome, having for the imperial colour the
same imperial hue; and though this preeminence in it applies to the human race itself, giving the white man ideal
mastership over every dusky tribe; and though, besides all
this, whiteness has been even made significant of gladness,
for among the Romans a white stone marked a joyful day;
and though in other mortal sympathies and symbolisings,
this same hue is made the emblem of many touching,
noble things . . . yet for all these accumulated associations, with whatever is sweet, and honourable, and sub-
lime, there yet lurks an elusive something in the innermost idea of this hue, which strikes more of panic to the
soul than that redness which affrights in blood.

This elusive quality it is, which causes the thought of
whiteness, when divorced from more kindly associations,
and coupled with any object terrible in itself, to heighten
that terror to the furthest bounds. Witness the white bear
of the poles, and the white shark of the tropics, what but
their smooth, flaky whiteness makes them the transcen-
dent horrors they are? That ghastly whiteness it is which
imparts such an abhorrent mildness, even more loathsome
than terrific, to the dumb gloating of their aspect. So that
not the fierce-fanged tiger in his heraldic coat can so stag-
ger courage as the white-shrouded bear or shark.

Bethink thee of the albatross: whence come those clouds
of spiritual wonderment and pale dread, in which that

white phantom sails in all imaginations? Not Coleridge first threw that spell; but God's great, unflattering laureate, Nature. . . .

I know that, to the common apprehension, this phenomenon of whiteness is not confessed to be the prime agent in exaggerating the terror of objects otherwise terrible; nor to the unimaginative mind is there aught of terror in those appearances whose awfulness to another mind almost solely consists in this one phenomenon, especially when exhibited under any form at all approaching to muteness or universality. What I mean by these two statements may perhaps be respectively elucidated by the following examples.

First: The mariner, when drawing nigh the coasts of foreign lands, if by night he hears the roar of the breakers, starts to vigilance, and feels just enough of trepidation to sharpen all his faculties; but under precisely similar circumstances, let him be called from his hammock to view his ship sailing through a midnight sea of milky-whiteness —as if from encircling headlands shoals of combed white bears were swimming round him, then he feels a silent, superstitious dread; the shrouded phantom of the whitened waters is horrible to him as a real ghost; in vain the lead assures him he is still off soundings; heart and helm they both go down; he never rests till blue water is under him again. Yet where is the mariner who will tell thee, "Sir, it was not so much the fear of striking hidden rocks, as the fear of that hideous whiteness that so stirred me"?

Second: To the native Indian of Peru, the continual sight of the snow-howdahed Andes conveys naught of dread, except, perhaps, in the mere fancying of the eternal frosted desolateness reigning at such vast altitudes, and the natural conceit of what a fearfulness it would be to lose oneself in such inhuman solitudes. Much the same is it with the backwoodsman of the West, who with comparative indifference views an unbounded prairie sheeted with driven snow, no shadow of tree or twig to break the fixed trance of whiteness. Not so the sailor, beholding the scenery of the Antarctic seas; where at times, by some infernal trick of legerdemain in the powers of frost and air, he, shivering and half shipwrecked, instead of rainbows speaking hope and solace to his misery, views what seems a boundless churchyard grinning upon him with its lean ice monuments and splintered crosses.

But thou sayest, methinks this white-lead chapter about whiteness is but a white flag hung out from a craven soul; thou surrenderest to a hypo, Ishmael.

Tell me, why this strong young colt, foaled in some peaceful valley of Vermont, far removed from all beasts of prey—why is it that upon the sunniest day, if you but shake a fresh buffalo robe behind him, so that he cannot even see it, but only smells its wild animal muskiness— why will he start, snort, and with bursting eyes paw the ground in frenzies of affright? There is no remembrance in him of any gorings of wild creatures in his green northern home, so that the strange muskiness he smells cannot recall to him anything associated with the experience of former peril; for what knows he, this New England colt, of the black bisons of distant Oregon?

No: but here thou beholdest even in a dumb brute, the instinct of the knowledge of the demonism in the world. Though thousands of miles from Oregon, still when he smells that savage musk, the rending, goring bison herds are as present as to the deserted wild foal of the prairies, which this instant they may be trampling into dust.

Thus, then, the muffled rollings of a milky sea; the bleak rustlings of the festooned frosts of mountains; the desolate shiftings of the windrowed snows of prairies; all these, to Ishmael, are as the shaking of that buffalo robe to the frightened colt!

Though neither knows where lie the nameless things of which the mystic sign gives forth such hints; yet with me, as with the colt, somewhere those things must exist. Though in many of its aspects this visible world seems formed in love, the invisible spheres were formed in fright.

But not yet have we solved the incantation of this whiteness, and learned why it appeals with such power to the soul; and more strange and far more portentous—why, as we have seen, it is at once the most meaningful symbol of spiritual things, nay, the very veil of the Christian's Deity; and yet should be as it is, the intensifying agent in things the most appalling to mankind.

Is it that by its indefiniteness it shadows forth the heart-less voids and immensities of the universe, and thus stabs us from behind with the thought of annihilation, when beholding the white depths of the milky way? Or is it, that as in essence whiteness is not so much a colour as the visible absence of colour, and at the same time the concrete of all colours; is it for these reasons that there is such a dumb blankness, full of meaning, in a wide landscape of snows —a colourless, all-colour of atheism from which we shrink? And when we consider that other theory of the natural philosophers, that all other earthly hues—every stately or lovely emblazoning—the sweet tinges of sunset skies and woods; yea, and the gilded velvets of butterflies, and the butterfly cheeks of young girls; all these are but subtle deceits, not actually inherent in substance, but only laid on from without; and when we proceed further, and consider that the mystical cosmetic which produces every one of her hues, the great principle of light, for ever remains white or colourless in itself, and if operating without medium upon matter, would touch all objects, even tulips and roses, with its own blank tinge—pondering all this, the palsied universe lies before us a leper; and like wilful travellers in Lapland, who refuse to wear coloured and colouring glasses upon their eyes, so the wretched infidel gazes himself blind at the monumental white shroud that wraps all the prospect around him. And of all these things the Albino whale was the symbol. Wonder ye then at the fiery hunt?

'HE TASKS ME; HE HEAPS ME'

Well into the voyage, Ahab contrives to win over the crew to his violent ambition. He nails a golden Spanish doubloon to the mast, the prize of the first man to sight Moby Dick. Tashtego, Daggoo, and Queequeg, the three giant harpooners, offer the Captain their knowledge of the white whale, but the first mate, Starbuck, a steady New Englander, argues with his Captain against the voyage of vengeance.

"Send everybody aft," repeated Ahab. "Mastheads, there! come down!"

When the entire ship's company were assembled, and with curious and not wholly unapprehensive faces, were eyeing him, for he looked not unlike the weather horizon when a storm is coming up, Ahab, after rapidly glancing over the bulwarks, and then darting his eyes among the crew, started from his standpoint; and as though not a soul were nigh him resumed his heavy turns upon the deck. With bent head and half-slouched hat he continued to pace, unmindful of the wondering whispering among the men; till Stubb cautiously whispered to Flask, that Ahab must have summoned them there for the purpose of witnessing a pedestrian feat. But this did not last long. Vehemently pausing he cried—

"What do ye do when ye see a whale, men?"

"Sing out for him!" was the impulsive rejoinder from a score of clubbed voices.

"Good!" cried Ahab, with a wild approval in his tones; observing the hearty animation into which his unexpected question had so magnetically thrown them.

"And what do ye next, men?"

"Lower away, and after him!"

"And what tune is it ye pull to, men?"

"A dead whale or a stove boat!"

More and more strangely and fiercely glad and approving grew the countenance of the old man at every shout; while the mariners began to gaze curiously at each other, as if marvelling how it was that they themselves became so excited at such seemingly purposeless questions.

But they were all eagerness again, as Ahab, now half revolving in his pivot-hole, with one hand reaching high up a shroud, and tightly, almost convulsively grasping it, addressed them thus—

"All ye mastheaders have before now heard me give orders about a white whale. Look ye! d'ye see this Spanish ounce of gold?"—holding up a broad bright coin to the sun—"it is a sixteen dollar piece, men. D'ye see it? Mr. Starbuck, hand me yon top-maul."

While the mate was getting the hammer, Ahab, without speaking, was slowly rubbing the gold piece against the skirts of his jacket, as if to heighten its lustre, and without using any words was meanwhile lowly humming to himself, producing a sound so strangely muffled and inarticulate that it seemed the mechanical humming of the wheels of his vitality in him.

Receiving the top-maul from Starbuck, he advanced towards the mainmast with the hammer uplifted in one hand, exhibiting the gold with the other, and with a high raised voice exclaiming: "Whosoever of ye raises me a white-headed whale with a wrinkled brow and a crooked jaw; whosoever of ye raises me that white-headed whale, with three holes punctured in his starboard fluke—look ye, whosoever of ye raises me that same white whale, he shall have this gold ounce, my boys!"

"Huzza! huzza!" cried the seamen, as with swinging tarpaulins they hailed the act of nailing the gold to the mast.

"It's a white whale, I say," resumed Ahab, as he threw down the top-maul; "a white whale. Skin your eyes for him, men; look sharp for white water; if ye see but a bubble, sing out."

All this while Tashtego, Daggoo, and Queequeg had looked on with even more intense interest and surprise than the rest, and at the mention of the wrinkled brow and crooked jaw, they had started as if each was separately touched by some specific recollection.

"Captain Ahab," said Tashtego, "that white whale must be the same that some call Moby Dick."

"Moby Dick?" shouted Ahab. "Do ye know the white whale then, Tash?"

"Does he fan-tail a little curious, sir, before he goes down?" said the Gay-Header deliberately.

"And has he a curious spout, too," said Daggoo, "very bushy, even for a parmacety, and mighty quick, Captain Ahab?"

"And he have one, two, tree—oh! good many iron in him hide, too, Captain," cried Queequeg disjointedly, "all twisketee be-twisk, like him—him—" faltering hard for a word, and screwing his hand round and round as though uncorking a bottle—"like him—him—"

"Corkscrew!" cried Ahab; "aye, Queequeg, the harpoons lit all twisted and wrenched in him; aye, Daggoo, his spout is a big one, like a whole shock of wheat, and white as a pile of our Nantucket wool after the great annual sheep-shearing; aye, Tashtego, and he fan-tails like a split jib in a squall. Death and devils! men, it is Moby Dick ye have seen—Moby Dick—Moby Dick!"

"Captain Ahab," said Starbuck, who with Stubb and Flask, had thus far been eyeing his superior with increasing surprise, but at last seemed struck with a thought which somewhat explained all the wonder. "Captain Ahab, I have heard of Moby Dick—but it was not Moby Dick that took off thy leg?"

"Who told thee that?" cried Ahab; then pausing. "Aye, Starbuck; aye, my hearties all round; it was Moby Dick that dismasted me; Moby Dick that brought me to this dead stump I stand on now. Aye, aye," he shouted with a terrific, loud, animal sob, like that of a heart-stricken moose; "aye, aye! it was that accursed white whale that razed me; made a poor pegging lubber of me for ever and a day!" Then tossing both arms, with measureless imprecations he shouted out: "Aye, aye! and I'll chase him round Good Hope, and round the Horn, and round the Norway Maelstrom, and round perdition's flames before I give him up. And this is what ye have shipped for, men! to chase that white whale on both sides of land, and over all sides of earth, till he spouts black blood and rolls fin out. What say ye, men, will ye splice hands on it, now? I think ye do look brave."

"Aye, aye!" shouted the harpooners and seamen, running closer to the excited old man: "a sharp eye for the White Whale; a sharp lance for Moby Dick!"

"God bless ye," he seemed to half sob and half shout, "God bless ye, men. Steward! go draw the great measure of grog. But what's this long face about, Mr. Starbuck? wilt thou not chase the white whale? art not game for Moby Dick?"

"I am game for his crooked jaw, and for the jaws of Death too, Captain Ahab, if it fairly comes in the way of the business we follow; but I came here to hunt whales, not my commander's vengeance. How many barrels will thy vengeance yield thee even if thou gettest it, Captain Ahab? it will not fetch thee much in our Nantucket market."

"Nantucket market! Hoot! But come closer, Starbuck; thou requirest a little lower layer. If money's to be the measure, man, and the accountants have computed their great counting-house the globe, by girdling it with guineas, one to every three parts of an inch; then, let me tell thee, that my vengeance will fetch a great premium *here*!"

"He smites his chest," whispered Stubb, "what's that for? methinks it rings most vast, but hollow."

"Vengeance on a dumb brute!" cried Starbuck, "that simply smote thee from blindest instinct! Madness! To be enraged with a dumb thing, Captain Ahab, seems blasphemous."

"Hark ye yet again,—the little lower layer. All visible objects, man, are but as pasteboard masks. But in each event—in the living act, the undoubted deed—there, some unknown but still reasoning thing puts forth the mouldings of its features from behind the unreasoning mask. If man will strike, strike through the mask! How can the prisoner reach outside except by thrusting through the wall? To me, the white whale is that wall, shoved near to me. Sometimes I think there's naught beyond. But 'tis enough. He tasks me; he heaps me; I see in him outrageous strength, with an inscrutable malice sinewing it. That inscrutable thing is chiefly what I hate; and be the white whale agent, or be the white whale principal, I will wreak that hate upon him. Talk not to me of blasphemy, man; I'd strike the sun if it insulted me. For could the sun do that, then could I do the other; since there is ever a sort of fair play herein, jealously presiding over all creations."

'AHAB DROPPED A TEAR'

Not yet having sighted Moby Dick, but knowing him near, Ahab
turns his thoughts for a few moments to the young wife he left at
home. Starbuck, sensing his chance, tries once more to turn Ahab
from his black purpose, and almost succeeds, but the chance comes too
late. Ahab invokes the determinism of God: he will pursue Moby
Dick regardless.

It was a clear steel-blue day. The firmaments of air and
sea were hardly separable in that all-prevailing azure;
only, the pensive air was transparently pure and soft, with
a woman's look, and the robust and man-like sea heaved
with long, strong, lingering swells, as Samson's chest in
his sleep.

Hither, and thither, on high, glided the snow-white
wings of small, unspeckled birds; these were the gentle
thoughts of the feminine air; but to and fro in the deeps,
far down in the bottomless blue, rushed mighty Levia-
thans, sword-fish, and sharks; and these were the strong,
troubled, murderous thinkings of the masculine sea. . . .

Slowly crossing the deck from the scuttle, Ahab leaned
over the side, and watched how his shadow in the water
sank and sank to his gaze, the more and the more that he
strove to pierce the profundity. But the lovely aromas in
that enchanted air did at last seem to dispel, for a moment,
the cantankerous thing in his soul. That glad, happy air,
that winsome sky, did at last stroke and caress him; the
step-mother world, so long cruel—forbidding—now threw
affectionate arms round his stubborn neck, and did seem
to joyously sob over him, as if over one, that however wil-

ful and erring, she could yet find it in her heart to save and to bless. From beneath his slouched hat Ahab dropped a tear into the sea; nor did all the Pacific contain such wealth as that one wee drop.

Starbuck saw the old man; saw him, how he heavily leaned over the side; and he seemed to hear in his own true heart the measureless sobbing that stole out of the center of the serenity around. Careful not to touch him, or be noticed by him, yet he drew near to him, and stood there.

Ahab turned.

"Starbuck!"

"Sir."

"Oh, Starbuck! it is a mild, mild wind, and a mild looking sky. On such a day—very much such a sweetness as this—I struck my first whale—a boy-harpooneer of eighteen! Forty—forty—forty years ago!—ago! Forty years of continual whaling! forty years of privation, and peril, and storm-time! forty years on the pitiless sea! for forty years has Ahab forsaken the peaceful land, for forty years to make war on the horrors of the deep! Aye and yes, Starbuck, out of those forty years I have not spent three ashore. When I think of this life I have led; the desolation of solitude it has been; the masoned, walled-town of a Captain's exclusiveness, which admits but small entrance to any sympathy from the green country without—oh, weariness! heaviness! Guinea-coast slavery of solitary command!—when I think of all this; only half-suspected, not so keenly known to me before—and how forty years I have fed upon dry salted fare—fit emblem of the dry nourishment of my soul!—when the poorest landsman has had fresh fruit to his daily hand, and broken the world's fresh bread to my mouldy crusts—away, whole oceans away, from that young girl-wife I wedded past fifty, and sailed for Cape Horn the next day, leaving but one dent in my marriage pillow—wife? wife?—rather a widow with her husband alive! Aye, I widowed that poor girl when I married her, Starbuck; and then, the madness, the frenzy, the boiling blood and the smoking brow, with which, for a thousand lowerings old Ahab has furiously, foamingly, chased his prey—more a demon than a man?—aye, aye! what a forty years' fool—fool—old fool, has old Ahab been!"

"Oh, my Captain! my Captain! noble soul! grand old heart, after all! why should any one give chase to that hated fish! Away with me! let us fly these deadly waters! let us home! Wife and child, too, are Starbuck's—wife and child of his brotherly, sisterly, playfellow youth; even as thine, sir, are the wife and child of thy loving, longing, paternal old age! Away! let us away!—this instant let me alter the course! How cheerily, how hilariously, O my Captain, would we bowl our way to see old Nantucket again! I think, sir, they have some such mild blue days, even as this, in Nantucket.". . .

But Ahab's glance was averted; like a blighted fruit tree he shook, and cast his last cindered apple to the soil.

"What is it, what nameless, inscrutable, unearthly thing is it; what cozening, hidden lord and master, and cruel, remorseless emperor commands me; that against all natural lovings and longings, I so keep pushing, and crowding, and jamming myself on all the time; recklessly making me ready to do what in my own proper, natural heart,

I durst not so much as dare? Is Ahab, Ahab? Is it I, God, or who, that lifts this arm? But if the great sun move not of himself; but is as an errand-boy in heaven; nor one single star can revolve, but by some invisible power; how then can this one small heart beat; this one small brain think thoughts; unless God does that beating, does that thinking, does that living, and not I? By heaven, man, we are turned round and round in this world, like yonder windlass, and Fate is the handspike. And all the time, lo! that smiling sky, and this unsounded sea!"

MOBY DICK

And at last the *Pequod* encounters Moby Dick. As the chase begins, Ishmael explains to himself the reasons for the dread he feels.

I, Ishmael, was one of that crew; my shouts had gone up with the rest; my oath had been welded with theirs; and stronger I shouted, and more did I hammer and clinch my oath, because of the dread in my soul. A wild, mystical, sympathetical feeling was in me; Ahab's quenchless feud seemed mine. With greedy ear I learned the history of that murderous monster against whom I and all the others had taken our oaths of violence and revenge.

For some time past, though at intervals only, the unaccompanied, secluded White Whale had haunted those uncivilized seas mostly frequented by the Sperm Whale fishermen. But not all of them knew of his existence; only a few of them, comparatively, had knowingly seen him; while the number who as yet had actually and knowingly given battle to him, was small indeed. For, owing to the large number of whale-cruisers; the disorderly way they were sprinkled over the entire watery circumference, many of them adventurously pushing their quest along solitary latitudes, so as seldom or never for a whole twelve-month or more on a stretch, to encounter a single news-telling sail of any sort; the inordinate length of each separate voyage; the irregularity of the times of sailing from home; all these, with other circumstances, direct and indirect, long obstructed the spread through the whole-wide whaling fleet of the special individualizing tidings concerning Moby Dick. It was hardly to be doubted, that several vessels reported to have encountered, at such or such a time, or on such or such a meridian, a sperm whale of uncommon magnitude and malignity, which whale, after doing great mischief to his assailants, had completely escaped them; to some minds it was not an unfair presumption, I say, that the whale in question must have been no other than Moby Dick. Yet as of late the Sperm Whale fishery had been marked by various and not unfrequent instances of great ferocity, cunning, and malice in the monster attacked; therefore it was, that those who by accident ignorantly gave battle to Moby Dick; such hunters, perhaps, for the most part, were content to ascribe the peculiar terror he bred, more, as it were, to the perils of the Sperm Whale fishery at large, than to the individual cause. In that way, mostly, the disastrous encounter between Ahab and the whale had hitherto been popularly regarded.

And as for those who, previously hearing of the White Whale, by chance caught sight of him; in the beginning of the thing they had every one of them, almost, as boldly and fearlessly lowered for him, as for any other whale of that species. But at length, such calamities did ensue in these assaults—not restricted to sprained wrists and ankles, broken limbs, or devouring amputations—but fatal to the last degree of fatality; those repeated disastrous repulses, all accumulating and piling their terrors upon Moby Dick; those things had gone far to shake the fortitude of many brave hunters, to whom the story of the White Whale had eventually come.

'HE'LL RISE ONCE MORE'

For two days the harpoon boats of the *Pequod* chase Moby Dick without success, and before the third and fatal day Ahab makes a prediction, at the same time claiming from Starbuck his absolute loyalty.

"Starbuck, of late I've felt strangely moved to thee; ever since that hour we both saw—thou know'st what, in one another's eyes. But in this matter of the whale, be the front of thy face to me as the palm of this hand—a lipless, unfeatured blank. Ahab is for ever Ahab, man. This whole act's immutably decreed. 'Twas rehearsed by thee and me a billion years before this ocean rolled. Fool! I am the Fates' lieutenant; I act under orders. Look thou, underling! that thou obeyest mine.—Stand round me, men. Ye see an old man cut down to the stump; leaning on a shivered lance; propped up on a lonely foot. 'Tis Ahab—his body's part; but Ahab's soul's a centipede, that moves upon a hundred legs. I feel strained, half stranded, as ropes that tow dismasted frigates in a gale; and I may look so. But

ere I break, ye'll hear me crack; and till ye hear *that*, know
that Ahab's hawser tows his purpose yet. Believe ye, men,
in the things called omens? Then laugh aloud, and cry en-
core! For ere they drown, drowning things will twice rise
to the surface; then rise again, to sink for evermore. So
with Moby Dick—two days he's floated—tomorrow will
be the third. Aye, men, he'll rise once more—but only to
spout his last! D'ye feel brave men, brave?"

"As fearless fire," cried Stubb.

"And as mechanical," muttered Ahab. . . .

So once more the sail was shortened, and everything
passed nearly as on the previous night; only, the sound of
hammers, and the hum of the grindstone was heard till
nearly daylight, as the men toiled by lanterns in the com-
plete and careful rigging of the spare boats and sharpen-
ing their fresh weapons for the morrow . . . while slouched
Ahab stood fixed within his scuttle. . . .

'*THUS*, I GIVE UP THE SPEAR!'

On the third day, true to Ahab's prediction, Moby Dick reappears.
Shipmates Starbuck, Stubb and Flask, aboard the *Pequod*, sight the
white whale and summon their courage; then Ahab in the longboat
turns to his task, to the final tragic attack, which the stricken Moby
Dick turns back upon the ship itself. Thus ends the book; in a brief
epilogue Ishmael quotes from the book of Job: "And I only am
escaped alone to tell thee!"

"The whale, the whale! Up helm, up helm! Oh, all ye
sweet powers of air, now hug me close! Let not Starbuck
die, if die he must, in a woman's fainting fit. Up helm, I
say—ye fools, the jaw! the jaw! Is this the end of all my

bursting prayers? all my life-long fidelities? Oh, Ahab,
Ahab, lo, thy work. Steady! helmsman, steady. Nay, nay!
Up helm again! He turns to meet us! Oh, his unappeasable
brow drives on towards one, whose duty tells him he cannot depart. My God, stand by me now!"

"Stand not by me, but stand under me, whoever you are
that will now help Stubb; for Stubb, too, sticks here. I grin
at thee, thou grinning whale! Whoever helped Stubb, or
kept Stubb awake, but Stubb's own unwinking eye? And
now poor Stubb goes to bed upon a mattress that is all too
soft; would it were stuffed with brushwood! I grin at
thee, thou grinning whale! Look ye, moon and stars! I call
ye assassins of as good a fellow as ever spouted up his
ghost. For all that, I would yet ring glasses with ye, would
ye but hand the cup. Oh, oh, oh, oh! thou grinning whale,
but there'll be plenty of gulping soon! Why fly ye not, O,
Ahab? For me, off shoes and jacket to it; let Stubb die in
his drawers! A most mouldy and over-salted death,
though;—cherries! cherries! cherries! Oh, Flask, for one
red cherry ere we die!"

"Cherries? I only wish that we were where they grow.
Oh, Stubb, I hope my poor mother's drawn my part-pay
ere this; if not, few coppers will come to her now, for the
voyage is up."

From the ship's bows, nearly all the seamen now hung
inactive; hammers, bits of plank, lances, and harpoons,
mechanically retained in their hands, just as they had
darted from their various employments; all their enchanted eyes intent upon the whale, which from side to
side strangely vibrating his predestinating head, sent a
broad band of overspreading semicircular foam before

him as he rushed. Retribution, swift vengeance, eternal malice were in his whole aspect, and spite of all that mortal man could do, the solid white buttress of his forehead smote the ship's starboard bow, till men and timbers reeled. Some fell flat upon their faces. Like dislodged trucks, the heads of the harpooners aloft shook on their hull-like necks. Through the breach, they heard the waters pour, as mountain torrents down a flume.

"The ship! The hearse!—the second hearse!" cried Ahab from the boat; "its wood could only be American!"

Diving beneath the settling ship, the Whale ran quivering along its keel; but turning under water, swiftly shot to the surface again, far off the other bow, but within a few yards of Ahab's boat, where, for a time, he lay quiescent.

"I turn my body from the sun. What ho, Tashtego! let me hear thy hammer. Oh! ye three unsurrendered spires of mine; thou uncracked keel; and only god-bullied hull; thou firm deck, and haughty helm, and Pole-pointed prow, —death—glorious ship! must ye then perish, and without me? Am I cut off from the last fond pride of meanest shipwrecked captains? Oh, lonely death on lonely life! Oh, now I feel my topmost greatness lies in my topmost grief. Ho, ho! from all your furthest bounds, pour ye now in, ye hold billows of my whole foregone life, and top this one piled comber of my death! Towards thee I roll, thou all-destroying but unconquering whale; to the last I grapple with thee; from hell's heart I stab at thee; for hate's sake I spit my last breath at thee. Sink all coffins and all hearses to one common pool! and since neither can be mine let me then tow to pieces, while still chasing thee, though tied to thee, thou damned whale! *Thus*, I give up the spear!"

The harpoon was darted; the stricken whale flew forward; with igniting velocity the line ran through the groove; ran foul. Ahab stooped to clear it; he did clear it; but the flying turn caught him round the neck, and voicelessly as Turkish mutes bow-string their victims, he was shot out of the boat, ere the crew knew he was gone. Next instant, the heavy eyesplice in the rope's final end flew out of the stark-empty tub, knocked down an oarsman, and smiting the sea, disappeared in its depths.

For an instant, the tranced boat's crew stood still; then turned. "The ship? Great God, where is the ship?" Soon they through dim, bewildering mediums saw her sidelong fading phantom, as in the gaseous Fata Morgana; only the uppermost masts out of water; while fixed by infatuation, or fidelity, or fate, to their once lofty perches, the pagan harpooneers still maintained their sinking lookouts on the sea. And now, concentric circles seized the lone boat itself, and all its crew, and each floating oar, and every lance-pole and spinning, animate and inanimate, all round and round in one vortex, carried the smallest chip of the *Pequod* out of sight.

But as the last whelmings intermixingly poured themselves over the sunken head of the Indian at the mainmast, leaving a few inches of the erect spar yet visible, together with long streaming yards of the flag, which calmly undulated, with ironical coincidings, over the destroying billows they almost touched;—at that instant, a red arm and a hammer hovered backwardly uplifted in the open air, in the act of nailing the flag faster and yet faster to the subsiding spar. A sky-hawk that tauntingly had followed the main-truck downwards from its natural home among the stars, pecking at the flag, and incommoding Tashtego there; this bird now chanced to intercept its broad fluttering wing between the hammer and the wood; and simultaneously feeling that ethereal thrill, the submerged savage beneath, in his death-gasp, kept his hammer frozen there; and so the bird of heaven, with unearthly shrieks, and his imperial beak thrust upwards, and his whole captive form folded in the flag of Ahab, went down with his ship, which, like Satan, would not sink to hell till she had dragged a living part of heaven along with her, and helmeted herself with it.

Now small fowls flew screaming over the yet yawning gulf; a sullen white surf beat against its steep sides; then all collapsed, and the great shroud of the sea rolled on as it rolled five thousand years ago.

EPILOGUE

"And I only am escaped alone to tell thee."

Job.

The drama's done. Why then here does one step forth? —Because one did survive the wreck.

It so chanced, that after the Parsee's disappearance, I was he whom the Fates ordained to take the place of Ahab's bowsman, when that bowsman assumed the vacant post; the same, who, when on the last day the three men were tossed from out the rocking boat, was dropped astern. So, floating on the margin of the ensuing scene, and in full sight of it, when the half-spent suction of the sunk ship reached me, I was then, but slowly, drawn towards the closing vortex. When I reached it, it had subsided to a creamy pool. Round and round, then, and ever contracting towards the button-like black bubble at the axis of that slowly wheeling circle, like another Ixion I did revolve. Till, gaining that vital centre, the black bubble upward burst; and now, liberated by reason of its cunning spring, and, owing to its great buoyancy, rising with great force, the coffin life-buoy* shot lengthwise from the sea, fell over, and floated by my side. Buoyed up by that coffin, for almost one whole day and night, I floated on a soft and dirge-like main. The unharming sharks, they glided by as if with padlocks on their mouths; the savage seahawks with sheathed beaks. On the second day a sail drew nearer, and picked me up at last. It was the devious-cruising *Rachel*, that in her retracing search after her missing children, only found another orphan.

---

*The harpooner Queequeg, anticipating the *Pequod*'s fate, had built himself a coffin which he was unable to use. It was attached to the ship with a spring-release so that it would bob to the surface if the ship went down.

POEMS

The public reaction to *Moby Dick* wounded Melville deeply, and
though he continued to write, he came to care less and less for publication. He supported himself as a customs inspector in New York City.
He wrote a long and confused autobiographical novel, *Pierre*, and
turned his attention to verse. Melville himself understood something
of his problem, and wrote about it to his friend Nathaniel Hawthorne:
"My development has been all within a few years past. I am like one
of these seeds taken out of the Egyptian pyramids, which, after being
three thousand years a seed and nothing but a seed, being planted in
English soil, it developed itself, grew to greenness, and then fell to
mould. So I. Until I was twenty-five, I had no development at all.
From my twenty-fifth year I date my life. Three weeks have scarcely
passed, at any time between then and now, that I have not unfolded
within myself. But I feel that I am now come to the inmost leaf of the
bulb, and shortly the flower must fall to the mould." It is not really
an accurate analysis, but it is Melville's own point of view. In fact, he
continued to write throughout his long life, producing poems, tales
and a brilliant novel, *Billy Budd*, which he wrote in the last three
months of his life. What follows is a brief selection of his poems.

THE RAVAGED VILLA

In shards the sylvan vases lie,
Their links of dance undone,
And brambles wither by thy brim,
Choked fountain of the sun!
The spider in the laurel spins,
The weed exiles the flower:
And, flung to kiln, Apollo's bust
Makes lime for Mammon's tower.

FAR OFF-SHORE

Look, the raft, a signal flying,
    Thin—a shred;
None upon the lashed spars lying,
    Quick or dead.

Cries the sea-fowl, hovering over,
    "Crew, the crew?"
And the billow, reckless rover,
    Sweeps anew!

MAD SONG

Stars laugh in the sky:
    Oh fugle-fi!
The waves dimple below:
    Oh fugle-fo!

OLD COUNSEL OF THE YOUNG MASTER
OF A WRECKED CALIFORNIA CLIPPER

Come out of the Golden Gate,
Go round the Horn with streamers,
Carry royals early and late;
But, brother, be not over-elate—
All hands save ship! has startled dreamers.

A RAY OF THE MOON

A ray of the moon on the dancing waves
Is the step, light step of that beautiful maid:
Mardi, with music, her footfall paves,
And her voice, no voice, but a song in the glade.

THE PORTENT
1859

Hanging from the beam,
Slowly swaying (such the law)
Gaunt the shadow on your green,
Shanandoah!
The cut is on the crown
 (Lo, John Brown),
And the stabs shall heal no more.

Hidden in the cap
Is the anguish none can draw;
So your future veils its face,
Shanandoah!
But the streaming beard is shown
(Weird John Brown),
The meteor of the war.

SHILOH: A REQUIEM
April, 1862

Skimming lightly, wheeling still,
The swallows fly low
Over the field in clouded days,
The forest-field of Shiloh—
Over the field where April rain
Solaced the parched ones stretched in pain
Through the pause of night
That followed the Sunday fight
Around the church of Shiloh—
The church so lone, the log-built one,
That echoed to many a parting groan
And natural prayer
Of dying foemen mingled there—
Foemen at morn, but friends at eve—
Fame or country least their care:
(What like a bullet can undeceive!)
But now they lie low,
While over them the swallows skim,
And all is hushed at Shiloh.

From CLAREL
Epilogue

If Luther's day expand to Darwin's year,
Shall that exclude the hope—foreclose the fear?

  Unmoved by all the claims our times avow,
The ancient Sphinx still keeps the porch of shade
And comes Despair, whom not her calm may cow,
And coldly on that adamantine brow
Scrawls undeterred his bitter pasquinade.
But Faith (who from the scrawl indignant turns),
With blood warm oozing from her wounded trust,
Inscribes even on her shards of broken urns
The sign o' the cross—*the spirit above the dust!*

  Yea, ape and angel, strife and old debate—
The harps of heaven and dreary gongs of hell;
Science the feud can only aggravate—
No umpire she betwixt the chimes and knell:
The running battle of the star and clod
Shall run for ever—if there be no God.

  Degrees we know, unknown in days before;
The light is greater, hence the shadow more;
And tantalized and apprehensive Man
Appealing—Wherefore ripen us to pain?
Seems there the spokesman of dumb Nature's train.

But through such strange illusions have they passed
Who in life's pilgrimage have baffled striven—
Even death may prove unreal at the last,
And stoics be astounded into heaven.

Then keep thy heart, though yet but ill-resigned—
Clarel, thy heart, the issues there but mind;
That like the crocus budding through the snow—
That like a swimmer rising from the deep—
That like a burning secret which doth go
Even from the bosom that would hoard and keep;
Emerge thou mayst from the last whelming sea,
And prove that death but routs life into victory.

'I LOVE SLEEPY FELLOWS'

Melville's correspondence during the second half of his life disproves the belief that he remained permanently embittered with the commercial failure of *Moby Dick*. In this letter to his brother, a sea captain, his joy and good humor are everywhere evident.

Pittsfield, Mass. May 25, 1862

My Dear Boy: (or, if that appears disrespectful) My Dear Captain: Yesterday I received from Gansevoort your long and very entertaining letter to Mamma from Pernambuco. Yes, it was very entertaining. Particularly the account of that interesting young gentleman whom you so uncivilly stigmatize for a jackass, simply because he improves his opportunities in the way of sleeping, eating and other commendable customs. That's the sort of fellow, seems to me, to get along with. For my part I love sleepy fellows, and the more ignorant the better. Damn your wide-awake and knowing chaps. As for sleepiness, it is one of the noblest qualities of humanity. There is something sociable about it too. Think of those sensible and sociable millions of good fellows all taking a good long friendly snooze together, under the sod—no quarrels, no imaginary troubles, no envies, heart-burnings, and thinking how much better that other chap is off—none of this: but all equally free-and-easy, they sleep away and reel off their nine knots an hour, in perfect amity. If you see your sleepy ignorant jackass-friend again give him my compliments, and say that however others may think of him, I honor and esteem him. As for your treatment of those young ones, there I entirely commend you. Strap them, I beseech you. You remember what the Bible says:

"Oh ye who teach the children of the nations,

Holland, France, England, Germany or Spain,

I pray ye *strap* them upon all occasions,

It mends their morals—never mind the pain."

In another place the Bible says, you know, something about sparing the strap and spoiling the child. — Since I have quoted poetry above, it puts me in mind of my own doggerel. You will be pleased to learn that I have disposed of a lot of it at a great bargain. In fact, a trunk-maker took the whole stock off my hands at ten cents the pound. So, when you buy a new trunk again just peek at the lining and perhaps you may be rewarded by some glorious stanza staring you in the face and claiming admiration. If you were not such a devil of a ways off, I would send you a trunk, by way of presentation-copy. I can't help thinking what a luckless chap you were that voyage you had a poetaster* with you. You remember the romantic moonlight night, when the conceited donkey repeated to you about three cables' length of his verses. But you bore it like a hero. I can't in fact recall so much as a single *wince*. To be sure, you went to bed immediately upon the conclusion of the entertainment; but this much I am sure of, whatever were your sufferings, you never gave them utterance. Tom, my boy, I admire you. I say again, you are a hero.—By the way, I hope in God's name, that rumor which reached your owners (C & P.) a few weeks since— that dreadful rumor is not true. They heard that you had begun to take to—drink? Oh no, but worse—to sonnet-writing. That off Cape Horn instead of being on deck

*Melville means himself.

about your business, you devoted your time to writing a sonnet on your mistress' eyebrow, and another upon her "Journal."—"I'll be damned" says Curtis (he was very profane) "if I'll have a sonneteer among my Captains."— "Well, if he has taken to poetry," says Peabody—"God help the ship!"—I have written them contradicting the rumor in your name. What villain and secret enemy of yours set this cursed report afloat, I can't imagine. — Do you want to hear about the war?—The war goes bravely on. McClellan is now within fifteen miles of the rebel capital, Richmond. New Orleans is taken &c &c &c. You will see all no doubt in the papers at your Agents. But when the *end*—the wind-up—the grand pacification is coming, who knows. We beat the rascals in almost every field, and take all their ports &c, but they don't cry "Enough!"—It looks like a long lane, with the turning quite out of sight.—Guert has recently been appointed to the command of a fine new sloop of war. I am rejoiced to hear it. It will do him good in more ways than one. He is brave as a lion, a good seaman, a natural-born officer, and I hope he will yet turn out the hero of a brilliant victory. —I don't write you, My Dear Boy, about family matters, because I know that the girls keep you posted there. But I will just say that of late Lizzie has not been very well, tho' she is now getting better. The children are all well. Macky is studying Latin—"Hic—haec—hoc"—"horum, horum, horum," he goes it every night.—And now, my boy, if you knew how much laziness I overcame in writing you this letter, you would think me, what I am,

Always your affectionate brother, *Herman*

AFTERWORD: 'DEATH BUT ROUTS LIFE INTO VICTORY'

The last line of Herman Melville's long narrative poem *Clarel* aptly applies to Melville himself. He died in bed on September 28, 1891, a man largely forgotten, his work neglected for years. But by the end of the second decade of the 20th century a new generation of readers and critics had rediscovered the great chronicler of the sea, and today his reputation stands at the front rank of American authors. If he was not our greatest writer, he was certainly one of the two or three great writers—Mark Twain and Walt Whitman being the others—this nation has produced. Herman Melville accomplished in *Moby Dick* the very goal Ahab set for himself, though he went Ahab one giant step farther and loved the whale as well as hated him. "In each event," said Ahab, "—in the living act, the undoubted deed—there, some unknown but still reasoning thing puts forth the mouldings of its features from behind the unreasoning mask. If man will strike, strike through the mask! How can the prisoner reach outside except by thrusting through the wall? To me, the white whale is that wall, shoved near to me. Sometimes I think there's naught beyond. But 'tis enough." For Melville also, it was enough.

IMPORTANT DATES IN MELVILLE'S LIFE

1819   Born August 1 in New York City.

1841   Whaler *Acushnet* sets sail from New Bedford with Melville aboard.

1842   Melville jumps ship in Marquesas and spends month with Typees.

1843   Ships on the *United States* as ordinary seaman.

1844   Debarks in Boston.

1846   Publishes *Typee*.

1847   Publishes *Omoo*. Marries Elizabeth Shaw on August 4.

1849   Publishes *Mardi* and *Redburn*.

1850   Publishes *White-Jacket;* moves, in October, to Pittsfield, Mass., and begins writing *Moby Dick*.

1851   Publishes *Moby Dick* to bad reviews.

1852   Publishes *Pierre, or, the Ambiguities*.

1853   In this typical year, *Moby Dick* sold 48 copies.

1863   Moves with his family to New York City.

1866   Appointed Inspector of Customs, a position he will hold for the next twenty years; publishes *Battle-Pieces*.

1876   Privately publishes *Clarel: A Poem and Pilgrimage in the Holy Land*.

1891   Dies at home on September 28.

1924   *Billy Budd* published posthumously.

INDEX